Santa's Elves
STICKER BOOK

Designed and illustrated by Stella Baggott
Written by Fiona Watt

Contents

North Pole

Sorting letters

Santa's elves are very busy sorting through Christmas-wish letters sent by children from all around the world.

Fill the pages with stickers of the mail being delivered and add an elf sitting at his desk.

WAY OUT

AIRMAIL

I ♥ XMAS

IN

North Pole

STOP

Making toys

Clonk... clunk... clatter! The elves are helping robots to make toy lions. One robot is painting the lions' eyes, another one is adding the clothes, while the yellow robot is sewing on their manes.

Press on the stickers of the busy elves and the half-finished toys.

Machine of the Month

Toy testing

All the toys made in the elves' workshop are tugged and pulled, prodded and poked, then played with to make sure they are safe.

Fill the pages with happy elves testing the toys for Santa.

New Toy FUN Factor

TOP SECRET

In the store room

The elves are rushed off their feet keeping the shelves filled with toys and making sure everything is tidy.

Use the stickers to help the elves stock the shelves with lots of toys.

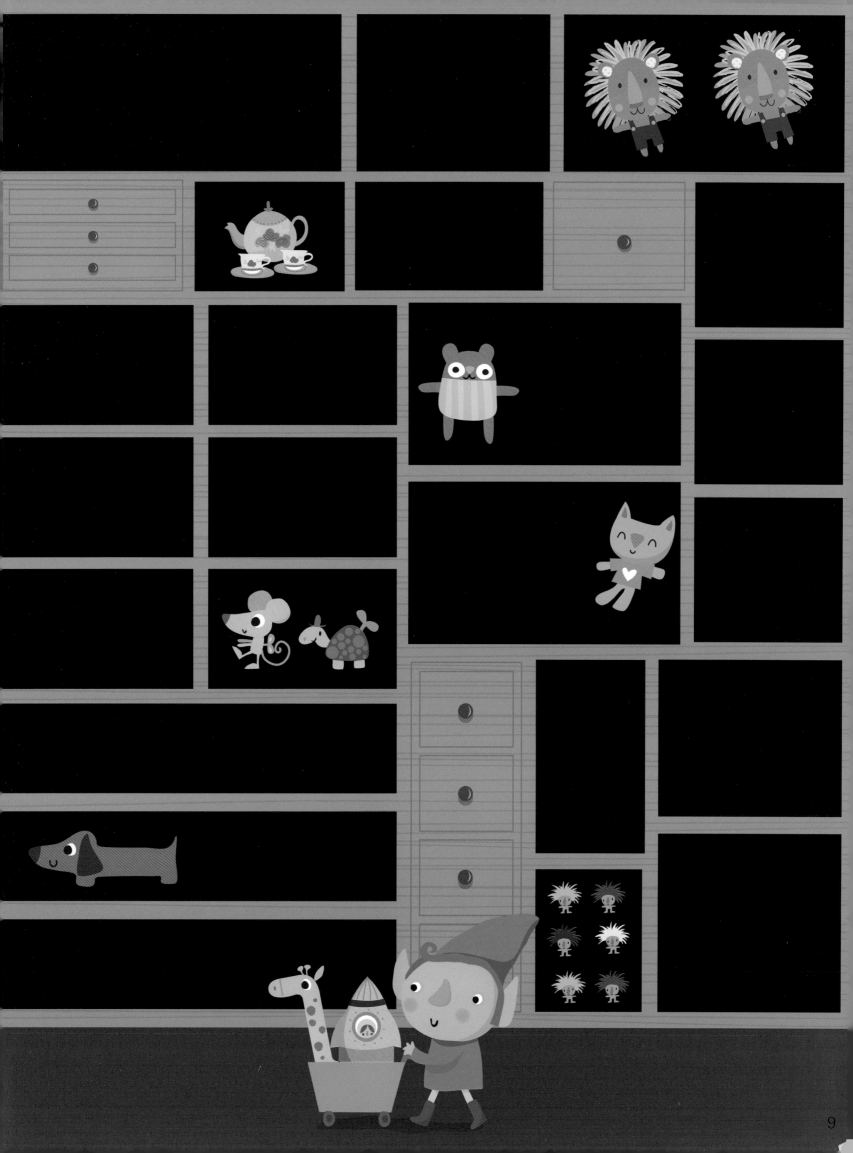

Wrapping presents

Two elves are operating Santa's amazing wrapping machine that puts presents into boxes, wraps them in paper and ties a bow around each one.

Fill the room with elves bringing toys to the machine and taking the wrapped ones away.

ALWAYS WEAR A HELMET

Ribbon Deluxe

Reindeer stable

During the busy weeks before Christmas, the elves prepare the reindeer for pulling Santa's sleigh. Then, on Christmas Eve, they track Santa's progress as he delivers presents to children everywhere.

Press on the stickers of the busy elves and the reindeer in their stable.

Office cleaners

The elves like to keep Santa's office neat and clean.

Place the cleaners around the office, and put the train bringing letters onto the tracks. Then, add the pictures and the clock to the wall.

Checking the sleigh

It's time to make sure that the sleigh is ready for its long trip on Christmas Eve. Some of the elves are checking the engine that will power the lights and keep the sleigh warm.

Fill the pages with elves cleaning and checking the sleigh. Then, press on the elf with a blue present onto the ladder.

SUPERSLEIGH 100

Baking treats

Making toys, wrapping presents and preparing Santa's sleigh make the elves hungry. These elves are baking some tasty treats for everyone.

Put the elves and bunnies around the kitchen, then add the cupcakes and trays of home-baked cookies.

Afternoon off

Occasionally, Santa lets everyone have time away from getting everything ready for Christmas Eve.

Use the stickers to fill the snowy slope and frozen pond with elves, mice and bunnies having fun.

Hot Chocolate

Party time

Every year, Santa throws a party for the elves to thank them for all their hard work.

Use the stickers to fill the barn with animals and elves having fun, then add stars to the slide.

Treats

At home

While Santa is away delivering his presents, the tired elves return to their homes.

Add the elf reading a book beside an open fire, then put the sleepy elves into the bedrooms.

Thank you

On Christmas Day, Santa never forgets to give all his elves a present, too.

Give all the happy elves a gift, then put the spare ones under the tree.

Sorting letters pages 2-3

Making toys pages 4-5

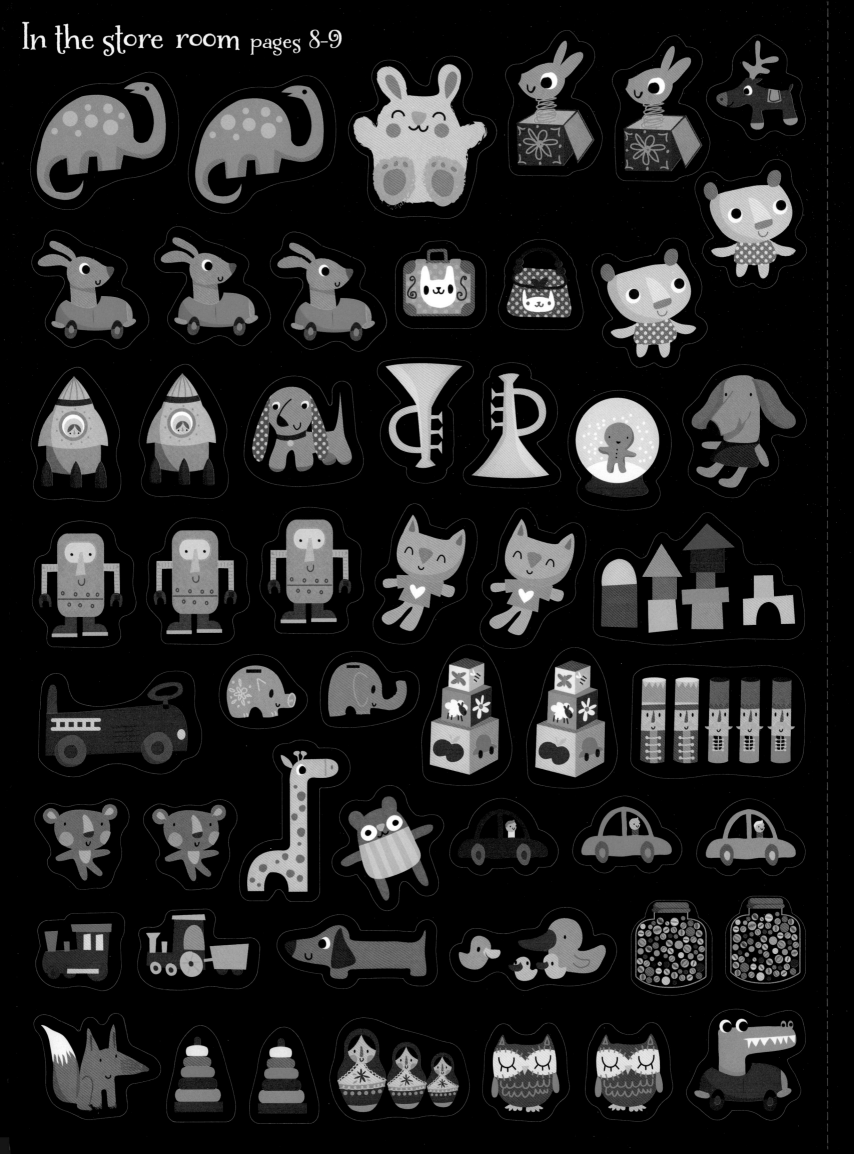

Reindeer stable page 12

Office cleaners page 13

THE BOSS

At home pages 22-23

Thank you page 24